What's Wrong?

ON THE MOVE

Catherine Veitch

Illustrated by **Fermin Solis**

Quarto is the authority on a wide range of topics.

Quarto educates, entertains and enriches the lives of our readers—enthusiasts and lovers of hands-on living. www.quartoknows.com

Author: Catherine Veitch
Illustrator: Fermin Solis
Designer: Victoria Kimonidou
Editor: Emily Pither

First Published in 2019 by QED Publishing, an imprint of The Quarto Group. The Old Brewery, 6 Blundell Street, London N7 9BH, United Kingdom. T (0)20 7700 6700 F (0)20 7700 8066 www.QuartoKnows.com

A catalogue record for this book is available from the British Library.

ISBN 978 1 78603 481 6

Manufactured in Shenzhen, China
HH112018

9 8 7 6 5 4 3 2 1

MIX
Paper from responsible sources
FSC
www.fsc.org
FSC® C017606

WHAT'S WRONG ON THE MOVE?

Hi, we're Leah and Eddie! Join us as we travel the world and discover all sorts of interesting vehicles.

But watch out! In each scene there are **five** out-of-place things. Can you find them all? Look carefully, as some are hard to spot.

Turn to the back of the book for handy explanations about what's wrong, as well as a **strange but true!** fact per scene – these might seem wrong, but they're actually right!

LET THE SEARCH BEGIN!

CONTENTS

FLYING HIGH

We're off to a flying start. There are so many ways to get off the ground but some are not possible today. Can you spot **five things** that are wrong or don't belong here? Can you say what's wrong with them? There are **two clues** to help.

One of these planes is over a hundred years old and doesn't fly any more.

I just saw a vehicle from another planet!

ON THE WAVES

Phew, it's good to reach dry land after that choppy crossing! Can you spot **five things** that are wrong or don't belong here? Can you say what's wrong with them? There are **two clues** to help you.

There's something cheesy about that yacht.

That's a strange place to read!

RIDING RAILS

The sights are whizzing by! Whilst you stop at this station and stretch your legs, can you spot **five things** that are wrong or don't belong here? Can you say what's wrong with them? There are **two clues** to help you.

This steam train ran around two hundred years ago.

That's a fun way to get off a train, but it's not right!

9

ON THE ROAD

This traffic jam will give you time to spot the next mistakes. The vehicles on this road are bumper to bumper and are hardly moving! Can you spot **five things** that are wrong or don't belong here? Can you say what's wrong with them? There are **two clues** to help you.

TAXI

I've spotted the first car invented. It's not around today.

There's something strange about the lollipop lady.

IN A SPIN

Are you ready to line up for some wheely great sport? Get set, go!
Can you spot **five things** that are wrong or don't belong here? Can
you say what's wrong with them? There are **two clues** to help you.

13

ON THE FARM

Vehicles do lots of jobs on a farm, including ploughing, sowing, harvesting and picking. Can you spot **five things** that are wrong or don't belong here? Can you say what's wrong with them? There are **two clues** to help you.

Cover your ears! Some tyres are about to burst!

Someone's fallen asleep on the job!

CONSTRUCTION SITE

Construction sites can be noisy places with hammering, drilling and digging, but there are lots of cool vehicles! Can you spot **five things** that are wrong or don't belong here? Can you say what's wrong with them? There are **two clues** to help you.

DANGER KEEP OUT!

Oops, the road roller driver has flattened the wrong thing!

That's a dangerous way to carry bricks.

SNOW TRAVEL

Get out your winter woollies. There are lots of ways to keep moving and stay warm here. Can you spot **five things** that are wrong or don't belong here? Can you say what's wrong with them? There are **two clues** to help you.

I've spotted someone's snow creation that's getting away!

They won't get far rowing on the snow!

RESCUE VEHICLES

The emergency services use lots of amazing vehicles to help them with their rescue missions on land, sea and air. Can you spot **five things** that are wrong or don't belong here? Can you say what's wrong with them? There are **two clues** to help you.

There's something slippery about the fire engine's hose.

One of those sirens looks too dazzling!

ANSWERS

FLYING HIGH

These **five things** are wrong in the picture:

(1) As far as we know, flying saucers or UFOs (Unidentified Flying Objects) are not real.

(2) We don't fly planes like this today. This was the first plane, built and flown by the Wright brothers in 1903 and called the 'Flyer'.

(3) This may be a fun way to walk the dog, but it's not possible to fly like this.

(4) Of course, aeroplanes don't have feathered bird wings. But people did strap big wings to their arms when they first tried to fly.

(5) There is no such thing as a flying carpet, but you can read stories about magic flying carpets in *The Arabian Nights*.

★ **Strange but true!** This flying car might look out of place, but believe it or not, companies are testing flying cars like this right now.

ON THE WAVES

(1) A bath is for bathing in and not for sailing!

(2) You can float on water in a rubber ring, but you can't sit on water like this!

(3) The wind blows against a yacht's sails to move it, but the wind would blow right through the holes on these holey cheese sails.

(4) Of course this hotdog isn't a boat, but the doggy thinks it's dinner-time!

(5) Elephants can't fly!

★ **Strange but true!** It might look weird, but this bus is meant to be in the water! Often called duck buses, these amphibious tourist buses can travel on both roads AND in water!

These **five things** are wrong in the picture:

RIDING RAILS

(1) This steam train was one of the first trains. It was made by George Stephenson in 1829 and was called the 'Rocket'.

(2) Train tracks aren't made from carrots! They are made from a very strong metal called steel.

(3) There may be a few slip-ups on this slippery slide! You'd normally take the stairs or lift.

(4) Of course, planes don't ride along train tracks! Planes do have wheels but these are let down for landing on solid ground.

(5) Trains can't fly – yet!

★ **Strange but true!** There really are hanging trains like this in Germany. The train lines were built above the ground because the land was hilly and flooded a lot

These **five things** are wrong in the picture:

ON THE ROAD

1. This car was one of the first cars and isn't around today. It was invented by Karl Benz in 1885.

2. Lollipop ladies and men stop traffic to help kids cross the road safely, but they hold 'stop' signs, not actual lollipops!

3. Some motorbikes do have sidecars that passengers can travel in, but a giraffe would be too big to ride with you!

4. These pizzas might look tasty, but they wouldn't make good car wheels! A car's wheels are made from strong metal with soft rubber tyres.

5. Roundabouts keep the traffic moving, but this cake roundabout wouldn't last long outside!

★ **Strange but true!** There is an ice cream van for dogs. It plays the Scooby Doo theme and sells gammon and chicken sorbet, and canine cookie crunch, which is a mix of dog biscuits and ice cream. Woof!

These **five things** are wrong in the picture:

IN A SPIN

1. This bicycle's wheels are wrong – it won't move with triangular wheels.

2. Roller skates have wheels and not springs. John Joseph Merlin invented roller skates over 250 years ago and he wore them to a party.

3. Flying wheelchairs haven't been invented... yet!

4. This person is on a surfboard instead of a skateboard. They should be in the sea – no wonder they are not moving!

5. Lobsters don't skateboard!

★ **Strange but true!** Most bikes have two wheels, but some have been changed like this to carry extra passengers. This parent can pedal the whole family, including their pet dog, to school!

These **five things** are wrong in the picture:

ON THE FARM

1. A tractor pulls many things, but a bed isn't one of them! Tractors can pull heavy loads as they have large, powerful engines and big wheels.

2. Did you spot the combine harvester with a banana attached to the front? A combine harvester has something called a reel at the front, not a banana!

3. Of course, it's not safe to transport a horse in a wheelbarrow! Horses are often transported in horse trailers.

4. Farmland is far too bumpy to ride a unicycle over!

5. These balloon tyres are going to burst – they won't support such a heavy tractor!

These **five things** are wrong in the picture:

★ **Strange but true!** Windmills were built on farms hundreds of years ago. Some windmills are still used on farms today to pump water and make electricity.

CONSTRUCTION SITE

 This flimsy digger's net won't hold much. Diggers can carry huge weights in their tough metal scoops.

 It may be a speedy way to get around, but you won't see builders wearing roller skates on building sites as it's not safe!

③ Oh dear, this road roller has flattened a car by mistake. Road rollers are normally used to flatten new roads and earth.

④ Did you notice this crusher vehicle has the head of a T-Rex? The T-Rex's jaws were so powerful that it could crunch bones in half.

⑤ The crane driver is not paying attention and has picked up a cow by mistake!

★ **Strange but true!** This may look like a giant bowling ball, but it's actually a wrecking ball – a heavy steel ball, usually hung from a crane, used for demolishing buildings.

These **five things** are wrong in the picture:

SNOW TRAVEL

① Snowmen aren't alive so they couldn't possibly ski downhill!

② This train has taken a wrong turn and shouldn't be going down a bobsleigh track.

③ Did you spot this ice-skating flamingo? Of course, flamingoes don't ice skate!

④ It might look comfy, but this sofa doesn't belong as a chair on a real ski lift!

⑤ This canoe is out of place as you would row a canoe on water, not on snow.

★ **Strange but true!** Believe it or not, this is really a snowmobile. It has been made by adding a snowmobile engine and skis to a car.

These **five things** are wrong in the picture:

RESCUE VEHICLES

① Monkeys don't ride scooters so this is wrong.

② Did you spot the police van's doughnut wheels?

③ Of course, helicopters don't have umbrella propellors!

④ This sparkling disco ball would be distracting as a siren! Usually police cars have flashing blue and red siren lights.

⑤ Oops this snake has been mixed up with the fire hose! Fire hoses are bendy like snakes but made of rubber with a tough material cover.

★ **Strange but true!** This robot is real. It's called a drone and scientists are building them to help with rescues.

These **five things** are wrong in the picture: